NUMBERS & COUNTING

Text by Billy Nigo
Illustrated by Bernard Adnet
Cover Illustration by Terry and Joe Chicko

Copyright © 1998 McClanahan Book Company, Inc.
All rights reserved.
Published by McClanahan Book Company, Inc.
23 West 26th Street, New York, NY 10010
Printed in China
ISBN: 0-7681-0090-9

one

groups of one.

2

two

☑ 2 🐷's.

☑ 2 ☀'s.

groups of two.

3  three

☑ ✏️ 3 🐱's.

☑ ✏️ 3 🧀's.

3

groups of three.

 3 3

4

 four

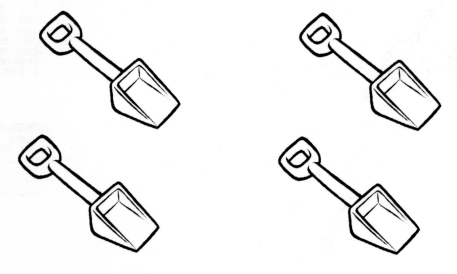

4 's.

4 's.

 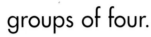 4

 groups of four.

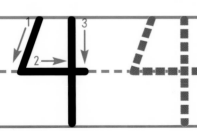

5

5 five

 5 's.

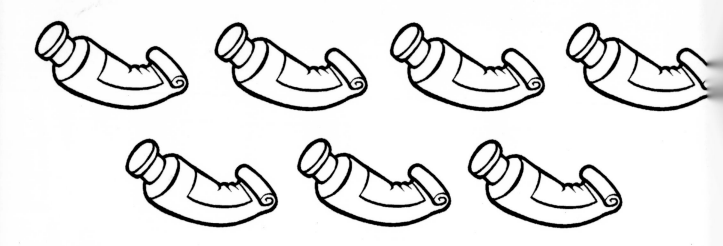

5 's.

groups of five.

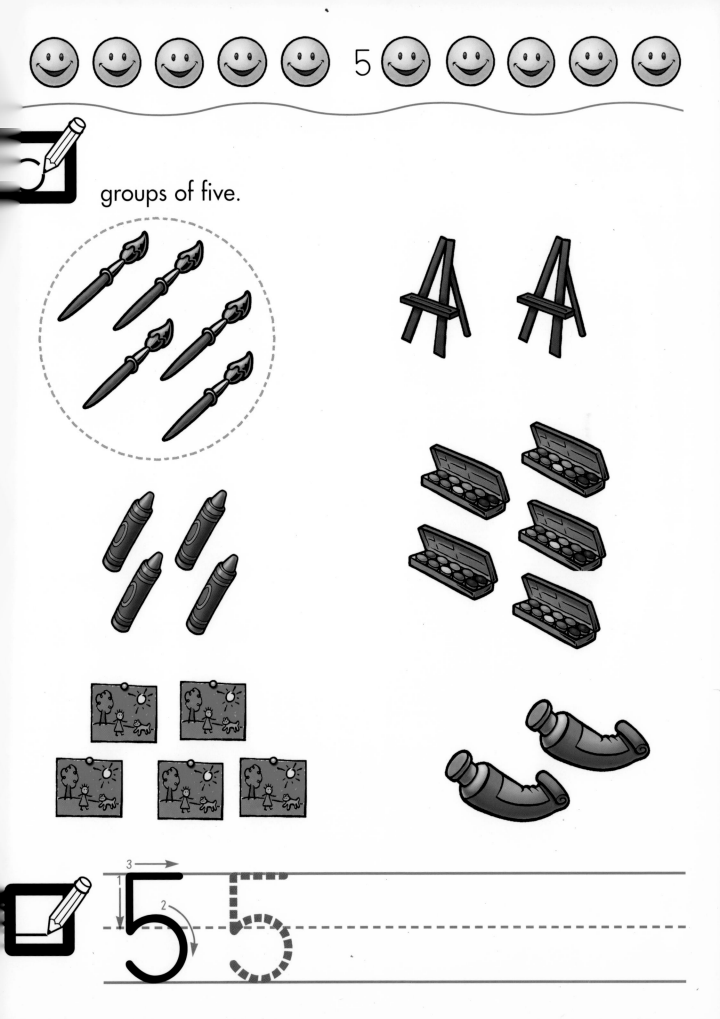

6  6

6 six

✏️ 6 🧸's.

😊✏️ 6 ◯'s.

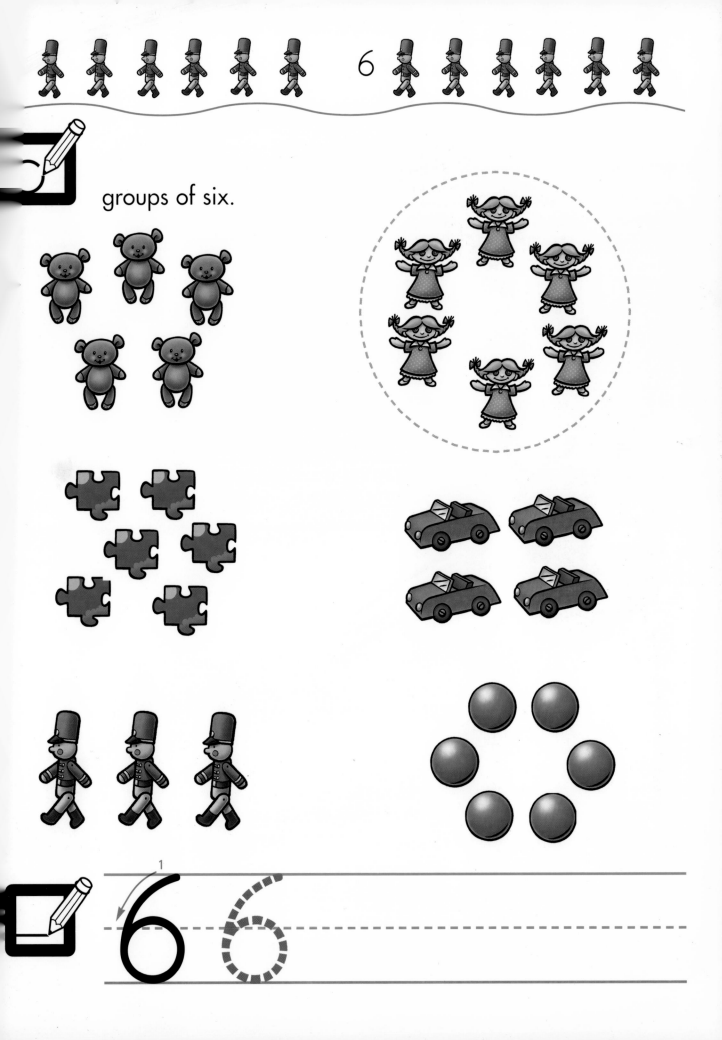

6

groups of six.

7

7 seven

☑ 7 🦋's.

☑ 7 🐍's.

groups of seven.

8  eight

 8 🌼's.

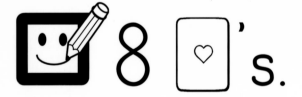 8 ♡'s.

groups of eight.

9

 nine

 9 's.

9 's.

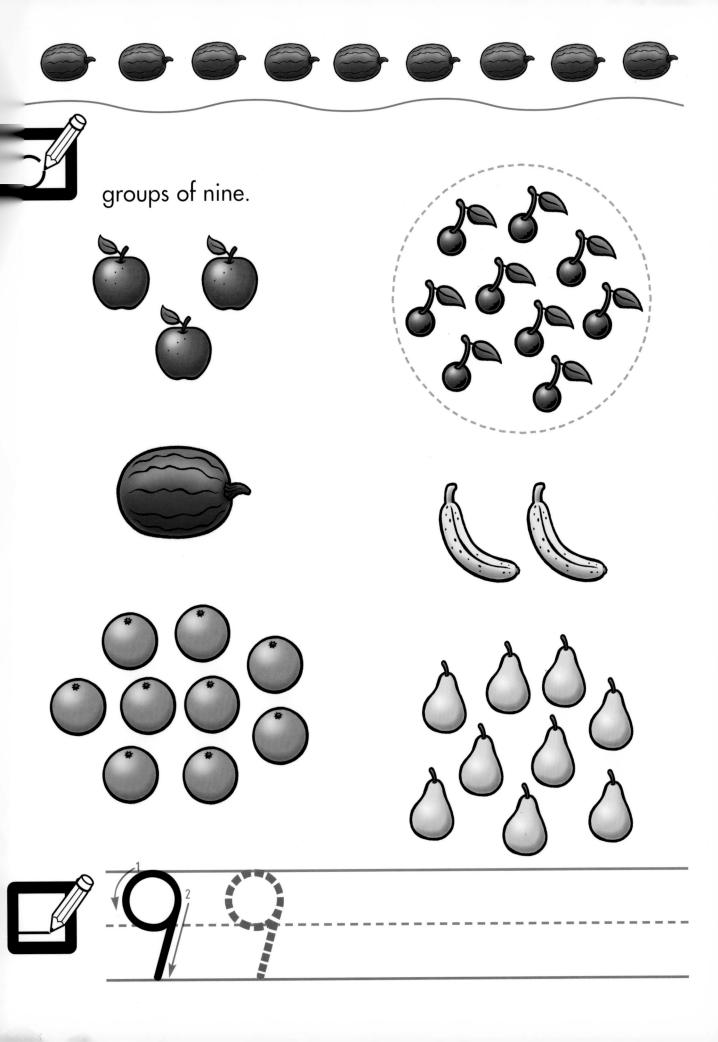

groups of nine.

10

10 ten

☑ 10 🧁's.

☑ 10 🍪's.

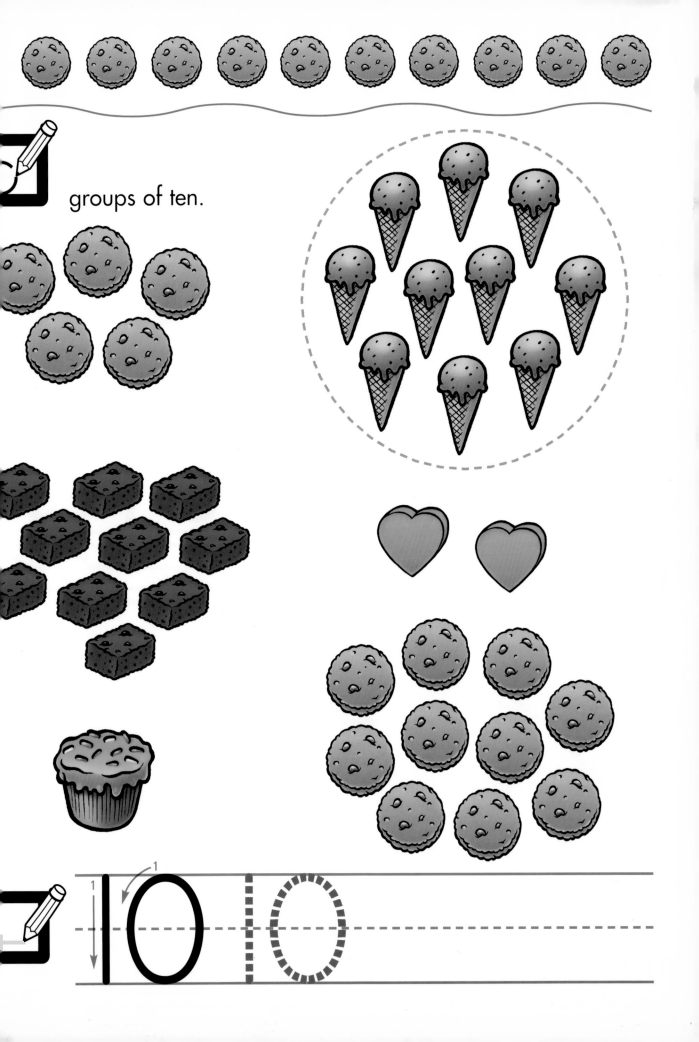

groups of ten.

Counting & Matching

1

3

5

7

9

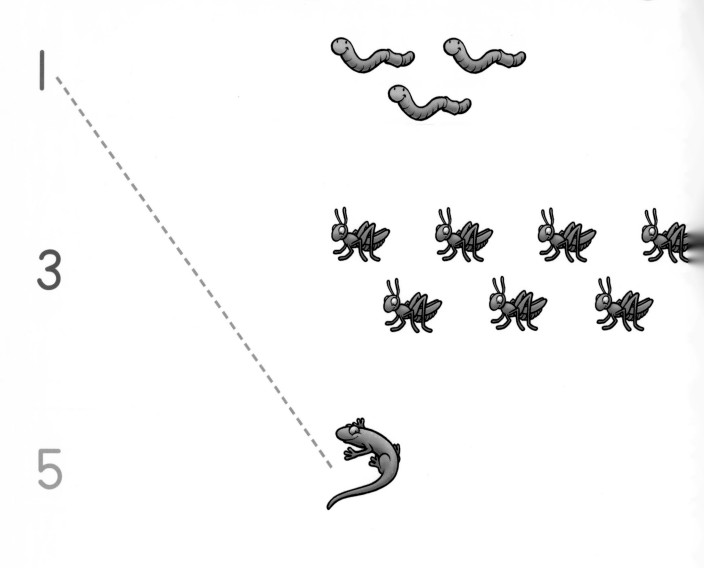